# THE ADVENTURES OF ISABELLE BOOK I: THE EMBRYO GODDESS AND THE MORPHO

Dearest Courtney,

Wishing you all the best on your heroine's quest!

nicole cutts

2018

Dearest Courtney,
Wishing you all
the best on

# THE ADVENTURES OF ISABELLE BOOK I: THE EMBRYO GODDESS AND THE MORPHO

By

NICOLE CUTTS

ILLUSTRATIONS BY WAYNE RODNEY

VISION QUEST PUBLISHERS

Vision Quest Publishers, a subsidiary of Vision Quest Retreats | www.visionquestretreats.com

Ordering Information:
Quantity sales. Special discounts are available on quantity purchases by educational institutions, corporations, associations, and others. For details, contact the publisher at dr.cutts@cuttsconsulting.com.

Printed in the United States of America
ISBN
978-0-9962901-0-4

First Edition

## DEDICATION

This book is dedicated to my nieces Cameron and Gabrielle, to my grandmothers Verona and Louise, to my father and mother Raymond and Carol Cutts and to all the little goddess-princesses out there and yet to come.

When you are sorrowful look again in your heart, and you shall see that in truth you are weeping for that which has been your delight.

Some of you say, "Joy is greater than sorrow," and others say, "Nay, sorrow is the greater."

But I say unto you, they are inseparable. Together they come, and when one sits, alone with you at your board, remember that the other is asleep upon your bed.

-Kahlil Gibran

The big question is whether you are going to be able to say a hearty yes to your adventure.

-Joseph Campbell

# PREFACE

In case you are wondering why I've written this fairytale or what you might get from it read on! I wrote this story because it is the sort of story I would have loved to have read as a little girl. I was not caught up in the princess craze: never aspired to be Snow White or Sleeping Beauty. The stories of fairy tale princesses of my childhood contained fairly one dimensional characters. They were often damsels in distress waiting to be saved by Prince Charming--never true heroines, or at least not what I thought of as heroines. These women were beautiful, to be sure, but not brave or adventurous; and none of them looked or acted anything like me. In short I did not see myself reflected in these stories and did not aspire to emulate these models that abounded in literature and cinema. Today I'm happy to see popular culture presenting more complex characters who reflect real heroism; and there is room for so much more diversity. I want women and young girls to see true reflections of themselves. I want them to know that they can be their own heroines and knights in shining armor and that they do not need to be asleep or in distress to find love or happiness. We find true happiness and love when fully awake and owning our power.

This book is also a reflection of my belief that all of us have an important mission and are on our own adventure; or, as Joseph Campbell would say, on a *hero's quest*. The Adventures of Isabelle tells the tale of the heroine's quest. Book I is just the beginning of her journey; her *call to adventure*. My hope is that, no matter where you are on your journey, this book will help you reflect on your heroine's quest and perhaps help you become clearer about your mission. We are all writing our own stories. This is mine and I hope you enjoy it and learn more about yourself while reading it. What's your story? Drop me a line at www.VisionQuestRetreats.com.

When one is on a heroine's quest she finds helpers and mentors along the way. To that end I'd like to thank a few people who have been integral in bringing this book to light.

As always I have to thank the Universal Spirit whom I choose to call G*ddess for showing me my mission and providing me with all I need to complete this mission while here on earth. I also want to thank my family and friends for their continued love and support. Thanks to my editors Tamara E. Holmes and Dr. Sanaa Sharnoubi, to my graphic designer Sherron Washington of The P3 Solution, and last but not least to my cousin, artist Wayne Rodney, for helping bring my vision to life through his wonderful illustrations.

# The Adventures of Isabelle Book I: The Embryo Goddess and the Morpho

## CHAPTER I

Once upon a time, not so long ago, there was a little goddess in embryo. Her immortal soul had been floating around in the cosmos when, at the moment of her conception, it had been snatched out of the universal atmosphere and brought to earth. She was to be born to mortal but royal parents in the kingdom of Xamayca. Her father, Vata Helios, The Sun King, was a magnanimous man who shone his warmth on all those he touched. Her mother, Cythona, The Ice Queen was a beautiful and imperious woman who ruled the palace with her steely will. They both loved each other very much; but their coupling was a strange one for at the moment when they came together the planets had been out of their usual alignment. Thus elements of both her mortal parents were in her; but there had also been trapped some other material, the origins of which no one knew.

When on the other side, she had asked to come to earth under these exact circumstances to further her soul's education; but as soon as she was born and felt the air around her it seemed to her that she had been duped. Before coming to this side she knew that she was a goddess, but soon after the moment of birth the forgetting began. Thus she felt as if she had been trapped.

"This," the baby goddess, whom they named Isabelle, thought, "is NOT what I had in mind."

She shouted to be let out, to go back to whence she came. She screamed through her first night on this strange cold planet, but no one could understand her. (That is why human babies cannot speak. They have just come from the other side and possess all the intelligence of the cosmos. The others, having been here for some time, have forgotten most, if not all of it, and do not want to be reminded that they now live in a universe of limited possibility. It is just too much for most former immortals to stand really.)

Nor was anyone able to comfort her. Her father and the nurses tried to no avail and her mother did not come. Because of complications in childbirth the palace doctor had informed her that she would not bear any other children. Her piercing cries rang throughout the palace warning all its inhabitants of things to come.

The princess looked like a normal enough beautiful baby human save for a few oddities here and there. She was a sort of reddish brown and had curly brown hair dusted with gold. Like her father, the Sun King, she had eyes the color of the late summer trees.

As she grew she became accustomed to this world and started to delight in the odd things she found here; rocks, water, trees, flowers, animals, insects; especially those pretty flying

flowers called butterflies. A special few of the other human beings were also very dear to her. She was drawn to anything that sparkled, especially the glint in her father's eyes. She recognized him from the other side and read in his smile a knowing of her too. She was sure it was him because of the one fleck of orange in his right eye.

Her mother, the queen, however beautiful and clever, was foreign and frightening to her. The goddess, now fully thinking of herself as one of them, tried to placate the queen with gifts of flowers and rocks and such, things she herself valued. She loved to play in the forest and during her adventures there would pick the prettiest little flowers to bundle up and tie with blades of grass. She was especially fond of the deep amethyst of the Dog-Tooth violets in the spring. These little offerings she would take and lay at the feet of the queen hoping to win her favor. Momentarily the queen would smile down on her but this never lasted for long. The queen was given to fits of rage and anger; and during her episodes she would sweep away anything that lay before her, whether it be a bouquet of flowers or her child.

The goddess, now a little girl, eventually had to give up placating the queen. She could never get it right anyway, could not be what the queen demanded. The girl, never having really let go her true origins, was somehow untamed. Like Artemis, she was most content when running wild in the forests and creeks of the kingdom; her pack of dogs, led by her favorite hound, Xerxes, following at her heels. She was often discovered on the hunt dressed in men's clothing, dirty hands and face, hair unkempt. She loved to ride her horses, especially her fastest, Philippides, a jet black Godolphin Arabian that stood sixteen hands, given to her by her father. She sometimes shamelessly rode bareback into the lake.

The queen tried everything she knew to tame her daughter; to turn her into a lady, someone who would be acceptable, who could attract her own wealthy prince one day. If the girl wanted to ride her horses or hunt with bow and arrow, the queen would suggest that she take up some other pursuits. Perhaps cooking, needlepoint or tapestry? When the girl played, rough-and-tumble, laughing (too loudly) with the other children in the palace, the queen would admonish her. The girl would look at her puzzled, not really hearing much but the phrases "not lady-like" and "unbecoming a princess," which were constant refrains. Even her father, who was amused by his spirited daughter, would attempt to domesticate her, discouraging her wild temper often reminding her to be "a nice girl."

At night, safely alone in her chambers the princess tried on the trappings of "a lady." She would bath herself in scented water, oil her skin, and fix her usually unruly hair in some neat style, put on a beautiful gown and sit quietly reading, writing or painting. She secretly delighted in this time. It was often during these sacred times that she would visit the gift her parents had received for her at her birth. The princess would steal down the long stone hallways to her father's private chamber where it was kept.

It was on her fifth birthday that her father had showed her the box and told her the story of the gift. After all the guests who had come for her party had left, her father had asked her to come to his study so he could give her one last present. She sat on his lap in his big comfy chair by the fireplace as he unraveled the tale.

*On the day that the queen had learned that she was pregnant with the princess, a strange woman dressed in white had appeared at the palace gates. She had come at dawn out of the fog on an unusually cold, late summer morning. This woman had clearly come a long way from the look of her shoes and clothing but she did not look tired. (The palace guard had noted this with some curiosity). Neither had his dogs barked, as they usually did, when strangers approached. He asked her to state her business. She told him that she had come on a mission from a far off kingdom and must see the king and queen. The guard sent a messenger to the palace and was surprised when word came back that the royal couple would see her. The queen was not prone to receiving uninvited visitors let alone those of the common variety, but the king had overridden her objections. The woman* was ushered into the room reserved for audiences with the royal couple.

The king and his queen sat regally in their respective thrones and waited for her to state her business. Refusing food and water she simply bowed before them and began. "I have come to bring you something that belongs to the daughter you are to bear in the spring." The queen was shocked. How did this strange woman know that she was pregnant? No one had been told, save for the king. She held her tongue and let the woman continue. It was at this time that the woman drew back her cape to reveal a most resplendent box. This box was the most unusual thing the queen had ever seen and yet it was somehow familiar. Oddly, the king seemed undisturbed by any of this as he sat quietly smiling at the woman. She stepped forward and placed the box in the queen's hands. The box, which was heavy and encrusted with all manner of gemstones, seemed to give off its own light. On the lid there was embossed an iridescent blue butterfly. The queen, an expert zoologist, who dabbled in entomology, recognized it as the Blue Morpho (M. menelaus). She had been fascinated by this creature in her studies and instantly recalled what she had read.*

\*The almost metallic blue color of the Morpho is not a result of pigmentation, the wings actually being clear, but is in fact a prime example of iridescence. The microscopic scales covering the Morpho's wings repeatedly reflect incident light at successive layers, leading to interference effects which depend on angle of observance as well as light wavelength. This is why the colors of their wings vary with the viewing angle. Although typically forest dwellers, Morphos do make forays into sunny clearings to warm their wings. With the exclusion of mating season, these butterflies typically live alone. The territorial male of the species will chase away any rivals.

Once exploited by the people along the Rio Negro in Brazil, the collected wings of the Blue Morpho were used for adorning ceremonial masks. Aside from humans, the Morpho has few predators. These creatures are poisonous due to the sequestering of poisonous compounds by the feeding caterpillar. From egg to death, the entire life cycle of the Blue Morpho is approximately 115 days. When this butterfly breaks free from its chrysalis, it will have less than a month to live.

*The woman spoke again. "You are being entrusted with this gift for your child. You must keep it in your possession at all times but you may never open it. Only she may do this at the time and place that she determines. It will be up to you to decide when to give it to her but be clear that it belongs to her."*

*The queen became indignant. Who was this common woman to tell her what to do with a gift for her child? She spoke up. "I trust you realize to whom you are speaking? Why should we take this gift from you and not look inside the box? How do we know you have not been sent to harm us? We do not even know from what foreign land you have come. How dare you*

speak to us like this? We do not want your gift and will not accept it! Get out!"

At this the woman rose gently to her full height. She seemed to grow a few inches before she spoke. In a low and even tone, she simply said, "This gift is not for you. It is neither for you to accept or reject. It belongs to the princess and she will have it whether you give it to her or not."

The queen fairly glared at the woman and was about to speak when the king laid his hand firmly on hers where it gripped her throne. He rose and spoke in a clear strong voice. "Thank you for coming all this way to bring this gift for our child. Her mother and I accept it graciously and will do as you have asked."

Looking into his eyes that glinted like sunlight off a forest pool, the woman smiled. She brought her hands together as if in prayer and bowed, first to him and then the queen before turning and taking her leave. The king took the box and left the chamber. The queen was furious at having been crossed and did not speak to the king for a full month after that.

Vata Helios had carried the box down the hallway to his private chamber. He had a special hidden alcove there in the wall. He drew back a heavy velvet curtain *the color of amethyst, opened the doors of this sort of tabernacle and placed the box inside. For just a moment he was overwhelmed by emotion and a powerful urge to open the box but he did not dare. His mind flashed forward to the future when he would bestow it upon his daughter, but for now he was content to keep it safely here for her. He closed the door and pulled the heavy curtain back over the space in the wall and returned to his duties.*

After telling her this tale he said "I am only showing this to you now but it is not time for you to have it yet. I will keep it here safe in this wall until the time is right. In the meantime you may see it and touch it but you are not to remove it from this room and you must not open it."

Sometimes toward the end of her secret nighttime sessions the princess would tiptoe down the echoing stone hallways to her father's private chamber. After quietly closing the door she would approach the far wall and draw back the heavy amethyst curtain before opening the small door to reveal her gift that lay in wait for her. She always delighted in the light that bounced around in the small space. She ran her hands gently and lovingly over the cool jeweled surface tracing around the butterfly with her finger. Then she would take a deep breath, steadying herself, before opening the box.

Remembering her father's admonition, she never opened it more than a crack. Even if she wanted to open it all the way and look inside to see its contents she could not. A brilliant blinding light would escape the tiny crack in the box and she would become overwhelmed by a power that threatened to engulf her. The feeling was indescribable; it mixed the threat of annihilation with such extreme pleasure and potency, the likes of which one could not imagine. She would approach the edge of madness before slamming the box closed again. Panting hard, sometimes sweating, it would take her a moment to collect herself before drawing back her hands. She always concluded this ritual by running her hands over the Morpho once more before bringing her fingers to her lips to kiss them and then placed this kiss on the butterfly. After bringing her hands gently to her heart in prayer she would reverse her actions, finally drawing the curtain back over the wall and quietly returning to her bedchamber. Once safely back in her room she undressed and lay on her bed before drifting off into the wildest dreams imaginable.

When the little girl became a young lady her relationship with the queen worsened. Boys, no longer just her playmates began to draw her fancy. Now the queen used this growing interest as a weapon with which to bludgeon our young goddess (who had all but completely forgotten who she was by now).

"Boys don't like girls who climb trees. How are you going to get a husband acting like that? Sit down, be still, be quiet, you're too loud."

It went on and on, criticism like water, dripping upon a stone. The girl was beginning to get worn down. Sometimes when she could no longer stand it she would run away. Hot tears streaming down her face, she would run away into the woods and hide, but at other times she would go visit her old friend in "the tower".

She had discovered her one day when after

one of her mother's fits of rage she was looking for some place to hide. She had run from the queen's wrath not knowing where she was going, barely able to see through her tears. She ran through the kitchen and through the servant's quarters, when she suddenly found herself at the foot of a narrow winding staircase that she had never seen before. She thought she had found a good place to take refuge so she quickly and quietly climbed the long flight of stairs. When she finally reached the landing she found herself facing a door that stood slightly ajar. She was startled to see a soft yellow light coming from within. She cautiously pushed the door open on its squeaky hinges and peered around the corner.

She nearly jumped out of her skin when her eyes met the face of an old woman with white hair drawn up in a bun on the top of her head. The old woman chuckled at her expression and beckoned her in.

"Come, come sit down." Not knowing why, she obeyed the old woman. Perhaps it was something about her kind amused eyes or her dazzling smile accented by her lovely pink lip-stick.

The girl wondered at her beauty. Until then she had always thought this sort of beauty belonged only to youth but she now saw differently. She was also a bit portly, as the girl would imagine a grandmother to be. She had to imagine because she did not have a grandmother of her own. Her father's mother had died before she was born and she had learned from the servants that her maternal grandmother, Isabel, had been banished from the kingdom by her mother many years ago upon her great uncle's death and her mother's subsequent ascendancy to the throne. She never did learn what the offense was that led to the banishment nor where the woman was living or if in fact she was living at all.

The girl took a seat across from the old woman, wiping away her tears, as she looked about the warm, cozy little room. The old woman regarded the girl for a moment, a look of pleasure spreading across her face before asking.

"Who troubled you?"

This was the first but not to be the last time the girl would hear this from her friend; but, for some reason upon hearing this question, she just burst into tears and told the old woman everything. She told her about the fits of her mother, and her attempts to break her spirit and she told her how she feared that she would never be able to please the queen, let alone get her to love her. It all just poured forth in one long stream of words and tears and not just a little bit of rage. The old woman reached for her, pulling the girl onto her lap, took her in her arms and held her until she was finished.

She held her and stroked her murmuring comforting words; then said, "She was not always like this you know. There was a time before, a long time ago when she was kind and full of wonder just like you."

"How do YOU know this?" demanded the girl as she looked into the old woman's face. "Who are you and why are you here in this room? Are you an old servant, past your time of working?"

With just a trace of bitterness the old woman answered. "Yes. I am an old servant. I served during the time of your mother's mother and at one time I cared for your mother. I tended to all her needs. We were very close then, but all that has changed now. When she married your father she no longer needed me. I was assigned other duties and eventually when I became too old to work I was sent here to the tower."

"But why were you allowed to stay in the palace? All the others are sent away or go to live somewhere in the village or countryside."

The old woman regarded the child carefully again then said, "Your father played a hand in it. They argued bitterly over it; but in the end I believe your mother never really forgot who I was to her when she was a child; so she acquiesced. I know to you she is only what you see now, but she could be very kind before. I also know that she loves you very much."

At this the little girl pushed the woman away

slightly, saying, "NO she does not love me. She loves only herself."

The old woman just shook her head and said, "In time you may come to see that the opposite is in fact true."

The little girl did not understand and right now she did not care what was meant by this. She was hungry and tired after her outburst. The old woman gave her sweet tarts to eat and hot tea with milk. After a long nap the child awoke and the old woman sent her on her way with a warning not to tell her parents of her visits lest the old argument was to arise. The child hugged her and made her way down the stairs.

She could hear the old woman whisper behind her as she descended the stairs, "Walk good."

The child laughed at her strange expression before turning to give her one last little wave at the bottom of the stairs. After that she secretly visited the old woman almost every day.

# CHAPTER II

Years passed and the young girl began to blossom into a young woman. Life at the palace continued pretty much as before. The king worked. He had an entire empire to run and a fleet of merchant ships. He often allowed Isabelle to be in attendance when he met with his advisors, and she learned much about his business and the affairs of state. Perhaps because he had no son, he allowed Isabelle to be trained in the arts of warfare and combat. She was adept with a sword and other weaponry, even competing in and winning many contests. Her mother discouraged this as she discouraged the other sort of lessons that the king allowed.

Isabelle delighted in these times that she spent with her father. One day he presented her with a model of one of their prized ships the Fragata Espanola. "One day Isabelle we will take a voyage on this ship and you must know how to command it. We will start with teaching you the various names of the parts of the vessel and how they are used."

Her mother interrupted. "Vata, I wish you would stop filling the girl's head with all this nonsense! When the time comes she will take up her rightful place of princess and that is here in the palace not on some boat with men. Can you imagine your navy taking orders from a woman?"

Exasperated her father replied, "Cythona for your information women can sail and command ships, and do. Isabelle as the rightful heir to my throne can choose to exercise her position as commander in chief of the armed forces of Xamayca as she sees fit. If she chooses to let Admiral Gravely do this she may, but she may choose to take a more active role, and she needs to be prepared."

Her mother, never one to be wrong, retorted, "The only women commanding ships are pirates. Do you want your daughter to be

a pirate?"

Unable to argue with such illogic, her father turned back to the instruction of his child while her mother stormed from the room in a semi-satisfied huff. "This ship has four masts, as you can see, and thirty six canons mounted on both sides. It's square rigged…."

It was also her father who taught her to ride. Starting her on a pony when she was quite small then gradually allowing her larger mounts. They would sometimes ride around surveying the kingdom together, she astride Philippides and he on his best horse; Xolotl. They would visit the villages and tenants to see how they were faring.

He taught Isabelle during these rides about the different industries often saying "It's important that you understand first-hand the workings of the kingdom because one day you will be called upon to lead and you must understand every aspect of what we do. Your mother and I will not live forever and while she may disagree, the time will come when all that I am teaching you will make sense."

Isabelle felt that the time that he spoke of was far in the future but she listened intently to his instruction and worked very hard to perfect her skills.

The queen, on the other hand, continued to groom Isabelle to take her place as a princess of another kingdom, while she herself commanded all those in the palace. Sometimes there were parties, sometimes trips abroad, sometimes visitors from other kingdoms. Occasionally a visiting family would bring a son; a potential suitor. During these visits the princess would sit quite still as she had been taught and focus on looking pretty. She could not hide the look of utter boredom on her face and some suitors, turned off by this, would go away shaking their heads. Others, in an attempt to engage her would suggest a walk around the palace grounds. Once out from under the watchful gaze of her parents, the girl would take these young men to see her horses. Unable to resist, she would invariably change clothing and suggest a ride. Once in her element she would challenge the young men to all sorts of games, archery, riding feats etc.

Some of these men she actually quite liked and for fleeting moments she could imagine falling in love and marrying, having someone to share her adventures with, a true partner, an end to her solitude. However, she had a most ungracious and un-princess like habit of playing very hard and often won out in these competitions. After a long while she and her new "friend" would return to the drawing room, her clothes and hair a mess, her cheeks red, eyes shining. The princes, gentlemen all, would look somewhat miffed and put out and would soon thereafter take their leave saying a polite "good bye" to the confused princess and her royal parents.

Her mother chastised her vigorously after these lapses from lady-like behavior. "You will never find a prince like this!"

The girl too wondered if she ever would find someone to love. Where was he and would he ever come?

The princess also took her lessons. Her parents hired the best teachers and had her receive instruction in all fields of study. She was continually discouraged from engaging in the old activities that she used to enjoy. Less and less did she hunt or fish or roam the woods. More and more did she dress and act as expected. The queen was pleased to see this change in her daughter. Perhaps all her efforts would pay off and the girl would yet find a husband to complete the process of domestication.

During pleasant weather, the queen would call round to the stable and have a carriage sent so she and her daughter could go for a ride through town near parliament house. During these outings the princess would sit stiffly beside her mother smiling faintly at those they passed. Her mother would chat with other ladies but was especially friendly to those rare acquaintances that had sons who would be suitable for marriage to her daughter. The princess would look on wearing an imperious expression, not unlike her mother's. She tried not to focus on her shoes that felt too tight and on the clothes that seemed ridiculous after a few hours. She also tried to ignore the immense boredom and utter lone-liness that she felt.

More than a few ladies would comment to each other later, "She is quite pretty."

"Yes, like her mother, but a bit cold."

"Yes, just like her mother and I hear she is quite impossible too."

"Yes."

Less and less did she ride out in the fields. More and more time did she spend indoors. She seemed to be trading her old adventures for a different kind: adventures of the mind. She spent many hours in the library reading and studying. Her father worried about this change; but her mother convinced him that this was a good thing, reminding him of how he had appreciated her mind when they met.

"She will please her husband by being able to keep up with him in conversation."

The king seemed uncertain but he let it die. He was at least glad that Isabelle still spent time with him, accompanying him to his business meetings and on other affairs of state.

There was one other change as well. The princess rarely visited her gift anymore. The last couple of times when she did, she had a strange reaction. Rather than enjoying the mysterious power, she felt ill afterward and had to lie still for a long time to recover from it. After one such episode she grew very weak and the palace doctor had to be summoned. She took ill with fever and slept for three days, only waking to drink water. After this she was in bed for a month. Even when she recovered she was very weak and wore a list-less expression upon her face. It was during this time that she made a curious discovery…

*One day during her convalescence she was sitting in the solarium taking some sun. She was alone and uncharacteristically bored. Some of her old spirit of curiosity and mischief was about her; so she decided to go exploring as she used to in the cellars of the cas-tle. She stood up on her weak legs, wrapped her wool shawl more closely around her and walked to the far end of the hall where the stairs led down to the cold and dank cellar. Once down there she found the usual* odd collection of cast-off things, furniture, bird cages, unwanted gifts that could not be thrown out.

Then she saw something she had never noticed before. Against the wall, partially hidden by an old painted Chinese screen, she saw a medieval suit of armor. It had long since lost its shine and was dark and tarnished. It's now dull surface was dark grey, almost black in fact, but something about it was very inviting. Beneath the armor was a cuirass, a sort of corset under the metallic torso that was made of very sturdy black leather. It was embossed with strange markings and laced up the back.

She decided to try it on so she took it off the dummy and put it on the ground. Then she unwrapped her shawl and took off her nightgown. She knew that this piece would normally be worn over some thin material but the material had long since disappeared so she put the cold leather directly on her bare skin. A strong shiver went through her whole body when she did this. Because it laced from behind she could not manage this part so she fixed it to herself as best she could. She wanted to see how she looked so she looked around for a mirror.

She found a full length mirror leaning against the

wall, moved the objects from in front of it then, using a rag, wiped away cobwebs and dust before standing before the mirror. She liked what she saw standing half naked before the glass with this unusual corset covering only her torso.

Suddenly and without warning the cuirass seemed to come alive, lacing itself up her back. At the same time, she felt instantly stronger and better than she had felt in months. She felt somehow electrified and stood up straighter, if a bit rigidly. She liked how it felt although she could not help noticing that it was a bit tight. Her breathing was not coming as easily as she would have liked. She tried to push this thought from her mind, enjoying the feeling of new-found strength instead. She turned this way and that, imagining herself in the midst of a fight, standing on the prow of a ship, or riding her horse into battle.

Just as she decided that she would keep it and wear it again she heard voices coming from the floor above. Her nurse was calling for her as she descended the stairs. Not wanting to take off the corset yet not wanting to be discovered like this, she quickly pulled her night dress on over it, grabbed her shawl and headed for the stairs. Later, safely in her bedroom af-

ter everyone had gone to bed she undressed again and stood before the mirror to daydream some more. Not for a very long time had she had such fun letting her imagination run wild. She did this until she let out a big yawn and realized how sleepy she was.

She began to undo the corset so she could climb into bed but something was wrong. Every time she tried to pull the free end of the string to release herself the thing tightened around her forcing her breath out of her lungs. The harder she tried the tighter it got. She tried to force it down from the top. She tore at the bottom with her now weak hands. She struggled until the thing got so tight that it threatened to cut off her air entirely! She wondered if she should call for help but knew she had better not. She panted loudly, panicked. What was happening? This could not be real. She decided to take a brief rest and try again to remove the now hateful garment. With all her strength she twisted and turned in an attempt to free herself. Finally exhausted, she began to cry. Looking down in despair she could see that the thing had now become a part of her! Worn out, she finally gave up for the night and fell asleep. Maybe she would have better luck in the morning when her strength had returned.

The next morning she awoke groggily with the sunlight streaming in the window on her face. She was recalling her horrible dream of the demon cuirass. What a nightmare! In her half sleeping state she began to stretch but stopped. Something was wrong. She put her hands on her body...no! Her hands felt the cold leather just as she looked down and saw it. It was not a dream! The black cuirass, with its strange markings, was still on her. She struggled for over an hour but try as she might, she could not remove it.

With a mixture of bitterness and excitement in her heart, she resigned herself to it. In some ways she liked the way it looked and especially how it felt. She felt protected by it and in a way it gave her strength; helped her to keep an erect posture; would no doubt support her when her energy flagged as it had begun to do in recent years. She also decided that she would tell no one because for some reason it shamed her and made her feel different. She had long ago grown tired of feeling different. No, she would tell no one. It would be her secret. So, on that morning she rose and dressed herself. She pulled her undergarments over this new feature of hers, and slowly buttoned herself into an elegant emerald green taffeta gown with malachite buttons. She would go for a ride in the carriage *with her mother as usual.*

After this, life at the palace continued pretty much as before. She continued her studies: history, political science, languages, dancing and painting. She still took her martial arts and fighting lessons, but most of her time was spent in the library. Rarely did she even ride her horses; and when she did it was a tame ride over the fields. No longer did she go galloping through the woods and streams, her head uncovered, muddying her clothes. She occasionally accompanied her father when he tended to matters of state and his business. He had acquired a new fleet of merchant ships that seemed to require much of his attention.

The queen entertained and ran the household. Occasionally suitors came; but the outcome was always the same. The princess almost never visited with her gift; on the rare occasions when she did, all she would do is look at the beautiful box with the iridescent Morpho inlaid on the lid. She could no longer tolerate the power it contained. Besides she

had her magical cuirass to give her strength.
What was in the box only made her feel ill.

# CHAPTER III

One day, not long after her sixteenth birthday, the princess accompanied her mother to the house of one of her close acquaintances, Lady Ann Seaworthy. It was the usual gathering of ladies of the court. They were having tea in the woman's lush drawing room. The ladies were prattling on about nothing, gossip really. The princess had long ago learned to listen with only one ear just in case someone addressed her. Occasionally a question was put to her. Usually it was about her studies. She did at least enjoy relating what she was learning to whoever asked. The current subject was ornithology. The women listened with polite amusement at her excitement.

"Did you know that the colors of the peacock plumage are actually due to optical interference? Some of their color also comes from pigmentation but the really brilliant color comes from a type of iridescence. They have nearly periodically arranged miniscule bowl-shaped structures found in their feathers. The various colors correspond to different scale length of these periodic structures. For example, for brown feathers, a mixture of blue and…"

One of the ladies interrupted. "I have heard that their brilliant color comes from a diet of thorns. Is this true?"

Before she could answer, the door of the drawing room burst open and their hostess turned toward it exclaiming with joy. The ladies, including our princess, turned to see what she thought was the most beautiful man she had ever seen. He was tall and he reminded her of the outdoors. His hair was the color of dry sand and his normally light skin was suntanned. His eyes too were like summer but also held the brilliant blue of the sky. Even the oldest women in the room seemed to preen as he entered.

He greeted them all warmly. "Hello ladies." Then addressing the lady of the house, "Good afternoon aunt." She stood up, and he gave her a big hug.

The girl felt something she had never experienced before. She felt warm as she placed her hand on her cheek and she felt suddenly shy, something she rarely felt, and even a bit dizzy. He glanced her way and gave her a quick smile. Had the others seen that? Had she imagined it?

Almost as quickly as he came, he left. He had just arrived to the countryside and would be staying with his aunt but did not want to interrupt their tea; so he grabbed a piece of cake off the table, kissed his aunt quickly and left the room. After this the princess was very distracted. She wanted to ask her hostess about him but did not dare. She knew that this behavior was exactly the sort her mother would call aggressive; so she held her tongue and waited for the others to ask. Eventually they did.

His name was Charmant and he was a prince. Apparently he was studying at a foreign university, something that had to do with banking. She could not be sure. He was here for the summer holiday, visiting his aunt and her two daughters. She was delighted to hear this last bit of information. She was sure to see him again, but when? She looked up and met her mother's eyes upon her, a knowing look on her face. The girl frowned and looked away.

For the next couple of weeks she found herself in frequent daydreams about this young, handsome man. She imagined riding with him, swimming in the streams and lakes in the countryside, and later sitting by the fireplace. She could not help thinking of him all the time, it seemed. One day her mother came to her and told her that they had been invited to a garden party at Lady Silvia's to be held on Sunday. She was glad to have something else to think about, something to distract her from her new found obsession.

On Sunday she and her parents rode away in the summer carriage to the party. It was a perfect day, sunny but not too hot. Big white clouds billowed across the sky. A light breeze ruffled her skirts as she climbed out of the carriage in the drive of the house where the party was being held.

She was sitting placidly looking around the garden when she noticed a small commotion. It seemed that several people were moving toward the house, specifically toward the French doors that stood open to the music room. She stood without thinking and followed the crowd. As she drew closer she could hear piano music and singing coming from within. She was not able to tell if the voice was male or female yet, but something drew her to it. It was beautiful, a low almost sad tune, somehow familiar and yet foreign. It awoke something inside of her, something that had gone to sleep a long time ago, long before the secret of the black cuirass, just before she had all but stopped visiting her gift.

She stood rooted to the spot, enthralled by the music, and closed her eyes to hear better. The song carried her away, back to a time of peace and innocence, back to a time when she was full of wonder. She could almost feel sunshine on her skin and hear the sounds of the forests in which she used to roam, hear the creek rushing as she rode through it on Philippides' back.

She stood like this for some time and was not even aware when the song ended. It was the sound of clapping that broke her reverie. When the crowd shifted and thinned she saw who had been at the piano. It was Charmant! He left the crowd and came over to her.

"Didn't I see you the other day at my aunt's house?"

"Yes but you came and left so quickly that I'm surprised you noticed me."

He laughed at this. "How could I not notice you? You were the only young woman there, not to mention your arresting beauty. I certainly saw you but I did not want to disturb the tea. I had hoped I would see you again; so this is my lucky day."

Unaccountably flustered she sought to change the subject. "Your playing was lovely. It was so peaceful. It reminded me of my childhood, when I played in the woods around here."

"It was actually this landscape that inspired the tune. I grew up in one very like this and spent many hours outdoors, hunting fishing, riding. It was an idyllic childhood, if somewhat lonely. I haven't any siblings and always looked forward to visits with family to play with my cousins."

Isabelle was impressed by this sensitive young man with a talent for music, so different from the others whom she had met. "I know what you mean, Charmant; only I don't have any cousins. I did enjoy times with the other children about the palace."

After this they spent the rest of the afternoon together, talking as if they were the only two in the whole world. He told her all about his studies and the foreign city in which he lived. She told him about her latest passions and about her favorite animals, going on for some time about Xerxes and Philippides. Rather than being bored or abashed, he laughed at the stories she told him of her many adventures. When the time came to part he asked if he might see her again. She agreed. They were to go out the next day. He would call on her around noon.

That night she barely slept. She wondered if this is what it felt like to be in love. It felt as if a thousand tiny butterflies had invaded her stomach. When her breakfast was brought to her in the morning she could not eat it. As the hour drew near she heard a knock on her door.

She gave a start as she thought perhaps he had arrived early, and she was not fully dressed yet. She was surprised to see her mother enter the room. She had come to admonish her to stay away from her usual un-lady like behavior, reminding her that she was a princess and that she should conduct herself as such at all times.

"It is unbecoming to be so eager; and please do not get out there and run wild. Men do not like women who act wild or are loud and boisterous. You should be quiet and demure and undemanding."

The princess suggested that perhaps it was better for her to be herself, but her mother interrupted her.

"You have plenty of time to be 'yourself' later. I'm just saying don't scare him off. I'm not suggesting that you not be you but perhaps you could just be a little less you. I've told you many times, men do not want a woman who draws attention to herself. They want a woman who helps them shine, who makes them look good. You must trust me."

The princess did not really trust her mother; but then her mother did have her father, and he was a charming handsome king; so perhaps she should listen. Isabelle made a promise to herself to be demure.

Prince Charmant arrived exactly on time, riding in a lovely carriage of the deepest mahogany with accents of burnished leather and copper. There were two black horses pulling it and there were two white horses, already saddled, attached by leads to its rear. As they pulled off she asked him where they were going. He told her that it was a surprise.

They rode along in relative silence, both smiling, looking out the windows, taking in the almost perfect day. There were many things she wanted to ask him about himself; but she concentrated on the passing scenery, feeling it was better to let him ask the questions, lest she appear too eager. Occasionally she turned toward him to find him looking at her. When their eyes met she quickly looked away. As the carriage rode on she noticed that they were entering territory that was unfamiliar to her. This surprised her as she thought she knew every inch of the kingdom. They were now passing through a large open field. She was delighted to see that it was filled with wildflowers of the most brilliant pinks, purples, blues and yellows. She wanted so much to get out here and collect all the flowers she could. Just when she could contain herself no longer and was about to ask to stop, the driver came to a halt in the middle of this beautiful field. Had he read her thoughts? They left the carriage and mounted the horses. He offered her a leg up; and forgetting her promise to herself to be demure, ignored him and mounted the horse without his help. The princess was excited, feeling her sense of adventure returning.

They walked the horses at a comfortable pace through the field of wildflowers, enjoying the sunshine and sweet smells in the warm dry air. Presently they came to the edge of a wood and entered its cool dark interior. She stole a look at the prince. She was so happy, being on an adventure with this handsome man. A few months ago she never would have imagined this; being with a young handsome prince, a man who was clearly interested in her.

The woods seemed to be alive. Birds and other small animals darted everywhere. She saw several Zebra Swallowtail butterflies, her favorites. She delighted in their irregular flight pattern. After some time she began to wonder again about their destination. She asked Charmant if they had a particular destination in mind. He asked her if she was growing impatient and if she would like them to hurry. Before she could even open her mouth to respond, he kicked his horse hard and took off with a whoop. She stood startled for one moment then followed suit. She caught up with him quickly, but he did not slow down. It had become a race, although she did not know where the finish line was.

They galloped through the forest, jumping over fallen trees and small creeks. She felt happy, alive and exhilarated. They tore on through the dark green interior of the forest, both focused only on the terrain in front of them and on reaching the unforeseen finish line. The two horses could be heard breathing hard. All four of them, the horses and their riders, had worked up a sweat. Just when she began to think that she could not go on any further, the prince started to lag and she happily pulled ahead of him.

She was becoming aware of a sort of dull roar in the air around them and vaguely wondered what it was. Eventually the roar became clearer and she realized that it was the sound of rushing water. Just then they broke into a large emerald clearing. The princess pulled back sharply on the reins as she saw where they had come to. They could go no further. Both horses came to a rather abrupt stop, panting hard, sweating. The princess walked her horse slowly to the edge of the clearing and found herself looking down into a deep ravine. They had come to the top of Crystal Falls; and the sight was breathtaking. She sat atop her horse for a long while, just surveying the scenery and breathing in the cool moist air. It smelled green and wet and lush.

The prince moved up slowly beside her. She looked over to see him smiling at her. He looked very pleased as he said, "So what do you think? Was it worth the wait?" She only smiled broadly in reply.

They dismounted, and he tied the horses to a nearby tree where they could drink from the stream and graze on fresh grass. He then unloaded their saddle bags and spread out a lavish feast on a quilt. In the center he placed a small copper vase and filled it with a bouquet of the bright wildflowers from the field.

She looked quizzically at the flowers. "When did you pick those? I never saw you do that."

He beamed at her. "I picked them when we first stopped. You were in the carriage."

He took her hand and bid her to sit down on the quilt. She did so, first taking off her boots. Then they ate, at first in silence, just looking around the wood and taking in the beauty. Then he spoke.

"You're different than I remember. I guess the tomboy has finally become the proper princess."

She was surprised and looked at him, her brow furrowed, trying to recall when they had met before. She stiffened almost imperceptibly before saying in a cool tone, "I'm sorry, but have I met you before?"

He chuckled as he answered "Not only did you know me, you used to torture me on an almost daily basis!"

"I'm sorry," she said, "but you are going to have to tell me what you are talking about."

Now he laughed aloud. "Yes I guess I will. I suppose I was just one of your many victims. I was a shy boy, small for my age, and no doubt made very little impression on you. We used to play together as children when I visited my aunt on summer holidays. I used to sneak away and come to play with the boys of the court and village. You were always picking on me for some reason or another. You actually beat me up on a few occasions. I somehow convinced myself that you picked on me because you secretly fancied me!"

It was now her turn to laugh. She vaguely remembered the prince now. He had been a scrawny child, somewhat insecure and timid.

"Maybe I did secretly like you or maybe you just got on my nerves. I'm so sorry if I tortured you though. I was a bit of a bully at times. I hope you can forgive me."

"Oh, I forgave you a long time ago. You actually helped me quite a bit."

"I did, how so?"

"Well for one thing every time you beat me in some game or another my friends teased me mercilessly. I vowed to get better and to one day garner the respect of my peers. I guess I used you and those times as a sort of reminder of who I never wanted to be again."

Although he spoke lightly, she could then see the hurt of the former little boy and was truly sorry.

Her tone was more serious as she explained. "Although I did not show it, I was often unhappy as a child. Let's just say being Cythona's daughter was not always fun. I am not trying to make excuses, but looking back I really think I often took it out on the other children. I am truly sorry."

The prince brushed it off. "Really, I'm okay. Look at me. I'm all grown up now." This last bit he said with a mischievous laugh, straightening up and striking a regal pose.

She smiled at him, while searching his face for any traces of the pain she had caused him. Finding none, she shook her head, pushed her empty wine glass toward him and said, Well then, let's move on. A toast to a fresh start?"

He nodded in agreement and they raised their glasses.

Then in a more sober tone he looked in her eyes. "Actually Isabelle you really did have an effect on me in another way as well."

He confessed that he had always had a crush on her but, as a child and as a young man, he was afraid to let her know. Her wildness and her brash manner had scared him before now; and he felt that she would never return his affections and that he would only be embarrassed, were he to express his true feelings. He had vowed to make himself into the sort of man that she would respect and admire. He had grown into a very handsome man and had finally become very popular both with his peers and with young women. He also confessed that he often asked his aunt for news of her and news of almost everything that she had gone through over the past several years that they had not seen one another. He heard the gossip about her wild ways and her mother's every attempt to marry her off to some suitor or another.

He knew too of her mother's growing concern of ever finding someone suitable for her daughter. He knew about her studies, her hobbies and he knew too that she spent most of her time alone, not really fitting in with the other ladies on the court. Finally he confessed that he had decided to spend his summer holiday at his aunt's estate to be close to her.

This was all too much for her somehow and she suddenly felt embarrassed, exposed and very vulnerable. She accused him of exaggerating and tried to make some joke or another, "Come on. Let's stop this serious talk. We came out here to have fun."

He looked at her, surprised by her reaction, but he did not waver. "I am not exaggerating Isabelle," he said emphatically "I think I'm in love with you!" Then more quietly, "I think I have always been in love with you."

She only stared at him, unsure of what to say next. She was saved by Mother Nature. Just then a Zebra Swallowtail flitted in between them and came to rest on the flowers in the vase.

"Oh, look." she exclaimed. "Have you ever seen a Zebra Swallowtail before?"

He looked at her, somewhat annoyed, answering coolly. "No, I can't say I have."

Undaunted by his obvious change in mood, she went on. "Well, this has always been one of my favorites. I used to collect butterflies when I was little. I wonder if I can still catch one."

At this she stretched out her hand slowly. The butterfly, feasting on the nectar of the wildflowers was in a sort of trance, her wings opening and closing slowly, rhythmically. The prince noted the rapt attention on her face as she stretched just a little closer; then, using her index finger and thumb, pinched the butterfly's wings together gently, stopping their opening and closing. She smiled broadly and, looking at the prince, held the butterfly out as if she was holding a trophy. In spite of himself, he had to laugh. She placed the creature on his arm and they both watched it for a moment before it flitted off again. After it was out of sight the prince suggested that they go exploring.

They spent the rest of the afternoon walk-

ing through the woods, climbing over fallen trees and moss covered boulders.

They followed the stream for a time and came upon a pool, deep and clear, perfect for swimming but when Prince Charmant suggested they swim, the princess, terrified of revealing the corset, said. "But I don't have my bathing costume, I can't swim in my dress."

The prince suggested an obvious alternative to the bathing suit.

She just rolled her eyes and suggested that perhaps they ought to be getting back as it was late. They walked in relative silence back to the picnic spot and packed up as the sun made her way toward the western sky. They rode out of the forest, which was almost dark now and back across the field in the gathering summer dusk. They made pleasant conversation in the carriage ride, recalling the highlights of the day. When he dropped her off at the palace he held her hand as he walked her to the door. She was self-conscious, aware of how hot her hand must have felt to his.

He bent and kissed her lightly on the cheek

before holding her away from him to look into her eyes. "I meant what I said in the forest today. I very much want to see you again. May I?"

All but forgetting her promise to herself earlier, she said eagerly "I would like that very much."

The princess practically floated to her chamber that night, dressed for bed in a dreamlike state, and slept peacefully. Her sleep was peppered with dreams, memories of Charmant as a boy. Different blurry scenes floated through her mind; but one dream she recalled clearly. They had been playing with a group of children (who they were she could not recall) and she had accused him of cheating at their game; she and Charmant had come to blows because of this. She had held him down and bloodied his nose; and he had cried, eliciting great ridicule from the boys among them. He had stormed off in a tearful huff, and she had felt somehow ashamed.

The next morning she was awakened abruptly by her mother, who was full of questions. What time did you get home; what did you do; and, worst of all, how did you behave? None of her answers did the queen find acceptable. When she learned of their wild ride she admonished the princess that she had no doubt scared Charmant off.

The princess retorted peevishly, "Then why did he ask to see me again?"

"Because that is what men do. What did you expect him to say? They will say what they think you want to hear. Stop being so naive! What did you say when he asked you if you wanted to see him again?"

For a moment she considered lying to her mother then said quietly, "I said yes."

Her mother let out a snort then, "Of course you did."

"Why wouldn't I say 'yes'? I do want to see him again."

"Because men like to chase, that's why. How many times do I have to tell you that? When you appear too eager it turns them off. I made your father wait a very long time before I agreed to let him court me."

She thought but did not say "Poor daddy." Instead she said "But I don't want to play games. Besides the prince is not like that. He likes me as I am!"

"Really?" That dangerous tone had crept into her mother's voice. "Really? He likes you as you are, huh? Men will say and do anything to get you to believe that. Don't! Trust me. Make him chase you. If he really likes you he will stick around. Right now all you have done is scared him off."

After this her mother ordered her to get up. They were to go shopping in the town. She wanted to say "no", that she had no interest in going anywhere with her mother. Her stomach was in knots, her mind awhirl, thinking about every word she had said to Charmant, thinking of the prince repulsed by her, pretending to like her. She felt shamed and just wanted to stay in her room by herself; but, before she could say anything, her mother barked, "Hurry up! Get up. We are leaving in half an hour!" She walked out, slamming the door behind her.

In the carriage Isabelle sat stiffly next to her mother. They did their usual rounds through the town, greeting other ladies and their daughters, stopping in several shops. She usually just took a seat in the corner while her mother tried on clothes and picked over jewelry, sometimes buying something, sometimes not. Occasionally her mother persuaded her to try on something. The princess was in no mood; but she submitted to this, all the while feeling bored and looking listless.

In one shop Isabelle was trying on a hat. As she regarded her visage in the mirror, she thought she caught a glimpse of a familiar face through the glass of the shop window. Her heart jumped and she turned just in time to see Charmant, walking past the shop next to a young woman that she recognized as one of the girls from the garden party, a girl she did not know but whom she had seen a few times before. The girl clung to his arm in a most irritating way. Without thinking she ran to the shop window and watched them walking away. The pair entered a small restaurant on the corner. She turned back slowly toward the interior of the shop and met her mother's scornful gaze.

"Oh well."

The girl was enraged but only said, "What does that mean?"

"It means 'oh well'. There are plenty of fish in the sea. What did you expect? Don't worry about him. Next time maybe you will do as I tell you."

After this the queen turned away from her and took up a conversation with her lady in waiting. She told her what to have sent to the palace. Then they went to lunch at the same place where she had seen the prince go; but he was nowhere to be seen. The princess barely ate and could not wait to get home to the privacy of her chamber.

When they finally got home, after what seemed like hours, the princess practically ran to her room. Once safely inside the door, she threw herself on the bed and began to cry. She cried for some time before sitting up and wiping her eyes. She looked calmly around her chamber now, watching the late afternoon sun stream through the windows, watching the dust swirl in the sunbeams. With a sniff, she wiped at her nose with the back of her sleeve. Maybe her mother was right after all. What did being herself get her? The prince was clearly not interested. But then why would he have said those things to her in the woods? She could almost hear her mother's voice, "because that's what men do."

She got up, resolving to move on with her day. She needed to move. She changed into her riding togs; pants, boots and a man's shirt and called for Xerxes.

She hugged him to her. "Hey good boy, you're a good boy, you're MY good boy."

They wrestled about for a minute before she rose and dusted herself off. They headed out into the warm early summer dusk, stopping to admire the lush greenery of the countryside from the terrace before heading to the barn. She greeted Philippides, who was happy to see her, having not seen her in some time. She scratched and tugged at his mane for a few moments before quickly saddling him, mounting and setting off. They rode out into the fields, going nowhere in particular. It was an easy ride. They alternately walked, trotted, then galloped through the countryside.

She could feel that Philippides was restless and, like her, wanted to blow off some steam; so, as they entered a wide open field, she kicked his sides and set him to an all-out gallop. She reveled in the feeling of the warm sweet air rushing past her head, filling her nose and lungs with it. The night was gathering now and the moon was rising above the hills before them. They rode on like this for some time. She noted that poor Xerxes was beginning to flag and knew he could not keep up for much longer.

"Just a minute more boy," she called to him as they took the small hill before them. As they neared the top she slowed and then brought Philippides to a halt. The three of them stood there silhouetted by the moon. She looked down on the valley before her, the cottages and landscape bathed in silver moonlight. She admired the beauty of it all and had all but forgotten about the prince by the time she turned and headed back to the castle.

She kept to herself for the next few days, spending her days in the library or painting in her studio. She loved to paint in the bright sunlight just after noon. As the dusk was gathering she would repeat the ritual of that night on the hill. Sometimes Xerxes would accompany her and Philippides, and other times he would choose to stay close to home, avoiding the arduous journey.

It was on the fifth night after the incident at the shop that something unexpected happened. It was a particularly hot night. She had been restless that day, finding it hard to concentrate on her studies owing to the oppressive heat. So after exercising Philippides, she stripped him of his saddle, stripped herself of her riding togs, and they all went for a swim. Xerxes had deigned to come with her; so he too got to go for a swim. She stayed on Philippides' back, holding onto his mane, feeling the cool water drift over them. It was pure heaven feeling the soft water caress her skin. Xerxes chased ducks along the bank, splashing happily.

After the swim she lay on a rock to dry. It was still warm from the day's heat and she enjoyed the warmth on her bare skin. Closing her eyes, she lay there for some time listening to the gentle snores of Xerxes who lay by her side. Something gentle made her open her eyes. It was a clear moonless night so she gazed into a black sky and could see almost every constellation. A shooting star blazed across the canopy of the sky just then; and she found herself making a silent wish on it. She wished for her prince, someone to share all this beauty with. After this she lay on her side for a while, listening to the crickets and luxuriating in the summer night. Then she dressed, saddled Philippides, woke Xerxes and headed home.

As she rode into the drive she saw a strange carriage parked there. It was rather late for visitors. Maybe her father had important business. She hoped nothing was wrong. She had a vague feeling of worry as she rode on past the drive to the barn. She left Philippides with the stable boy and entered the house from the back terrace. She heard laughter coming from the drawing room and as she drew closer she could make out the voice of her mother and then her friend, Lady Seaworthy. "Yes we just got back from the house on the coast. I told Charmant it was too late to call but he insisted."

The queen replied in her most gracious voice, "Oh not at all my dear. We are happy to see you and your dear niece and nephew."

The princess came around the corner and her heart nearly stopped. There sat the prince next to the girl she had seen him with the other day. She stared for a moment before her mother's voice broke her trance. "Oh, dear, you remember Charmant? And this is his cousin Lilian. She is visiting with her aunt for the summer too."

The princess extended her hand slowly,

feeling somewhat self-conscious in her dirty riding pants and shirt, her hair a mess. She barely glanced at the prince before taking a seat across from them on the couch next to her mother. Xerxes tried to jump up on the couch to take his seat next to her, but the princess gently pushed him off the couch then sat stroking his head.

Then Charmant spoke to her. "So how have you been?" Nothing in his tone gave away whether he knew what she had gone through for the past five days. She said that she had been well and inquired about him.

She learned then, that his cousin had arrived the day after their picnic and the Seaworthy's had set off on an impromptu holiday to their villa on the coast. "We had a great time. You should come next time we go. Lilly doesn't know too many people here; so it would have been good for her. We are at school together. We decided to go at the last minute or I would have asked you."

Lilly agreed. She was a charming girl. Now that she had a closer look, the princess could easily see the family resemblance.

Isabelle so wanted to ask Charmant why he had not written but knew she could not ask in front of his family and her mother. Just then Lady Seaworthy spoke. "Well we really have to get going now. It's very late." Then she shot Isabelle a knowing look before saying, "Charmant really insisted that we stop but we must be going now. Isabelle please come to see us soon? I know Charmant and Lilly would like this very much."

The next day Charmant came to call; and almost every day after that they were together. Sometimes Lilly accompanied them, but most times they were alone. It was an idyllic summer: riding their horses over almost every inch of the kingdom, swimming at Crystal Falls (Isabelle was always sure to wear her bathing costume and a shirt), and the occasional weekend at the coast. There were several parties, dances in the moonlight. Every moment apart was a torture and she looked forward to the moments when they would be together. She no longer felt alone. One day in late summer they rode their horses to Mr. Butler's farm. The berries were ripe, and they went to pick them. They lay in the grass, eating the hot sweet berries and kissing. He had suddenly grabbed her to him almost violently and asked "Why won't you say it?"

She did not know what he meant. "Say what? What are you talking about?"

"You know what I mean. You never say 'I love you.' I love you and I've told you; but you never say it to me. Do you not love me?"

The princess demurred, saying, "I don't know what that means. I feel for you a lot, but why do I have to say it?"

Then after a long pause she said quietly, "Yes, I suppose I do love you."

She had said it and she meant it. She realized in that moment that she had been afraid; but, that yes, she had come to truly love Charmant.

After this day they spoke of their future often. He was to return to school and finish in two years. They planned to marry then.

They would tell no one of their engagement. He thought it better to wait, to avoid the prying eyes and minds of the lords and ladies of the court for as long as they could. The princess was ecstatic and more than happy to keep this delicious secret to herself.

One very hot late summer afternoon Isabelle and Charmant were off riding. They had raced to the base of the falls, one of their favorite things to do. Sweating they had just dismounted their horses when it began to rain. It was one of those hot summer rains that you don't run from. He had suddenly taken her in his arms and began to kiss her wildly. Then he undressed and ran into the clear pool beckoning for her to follow him. For a moment she was frozen. She had never been naked in front of him, or any man for that matter. It was not her nudity that worried her but the terrible secret of her cuirass that she had managed to hide from everyone.

She stripped off her pants and riding jacket, leaving on her shirt and ran into the pool after him. Once there, they continued kissing, splashing, and writhing around in the water. Things were really starting to heat up when a loud clap of thunder rang out in the forest. The horses were getting spooked and pulling at their leads when a streak of lightning hit a tree not ten yards from them. Without a word they scrambled out of the pool, pulled on their soaking clothes, mounted their horses and sped away. They rode up to the Seaworthy's house, panting and out of breath. They entered the foyer, laughing and exclaiming at their good fortune to have gotten out of the woods before being struck by lightning. Their voices echoed off the walls. A male servant entered the hall and, in one breath Charmant asked him to make up a fire in the small parlor and inquired about his aunt and cousins. He was informed that they had all gone out.

Charmant took Isabelle's hand and led her into the parlor. He poured some brandy for her and, handing her a towel, turned to pour one for him. She wrapped the towel around her shoulders and went and stood before the fire sipping her drink slowly. He came up behind her and lifting the towel off her shoulders, began to dry her hair. He took fresh towels and dried her from head to toe before beginning to take off her jacket. Between the brandy and the growing heat she found it hard to resist.

He laid a plush quilt down in front of the fire before pulling her to the floor where he helped her out of her pants. She shivered a bit then. He noticed her empty glass and got up to pour her another, then placed the bottle on the floor next to them before the fire place. She sat sipping from her glass as he undressed. She was hugging her knees to her chest, watching him lay their clothes on the iron screen on the hearth. The firelight danced off of his honey colored skin. She was burning up when he took the glass from her hand and began to unbutton her shirt. She pushed his hand away and shook her head. He kissed her on the mouth and she returned the kisses. He tried again to unbutton her shirt and again she resisted.

He held her away from him to look into her eyes. He asked her, "Don't you trust me?

I thought you loved me."

How could she explain that it was not what he thought? She tried to convince him that she did trust him and that she did love him; but she was afraid that he would not love her if he understood.

"Understood what Isabelle? I love you and nothing can change that. Please you have to trust me."

She finally relented and let him undress her completely. He lay there quietly for a time, looking at the odd contraption on her torso. She was terrified then, terrified that what she thought was true. He would not, could not, love her now that he knew her terrible secret; the ugly "garment" that she wore, worse, that she needed to wear. She began to cry. This seemed to break him out of his reverie.

Looking confused, he gathered her into his arms. He asked her why she was crying. She poured out the entire story of the dreaded cuirass to him, concluding with her fear that discovery by him would lead him to reject her. He laughed gently at her. He explained that this changed nothing, that he loved her and always would. He kissed away her tears. He held himself over her and she smiled into his eyes, now the color of sea glass. She ran her hands through his sandy curls and hugged him to her. He whispered into her ear, "I love you."

She had never made love with a man before. She was scared and excited, anticipating what was about to happen. Just then they heard a loud knock at the door. He jumped up pulling on his clothes hastily. She tried to do the same as he moved toward the closed parlor door. She imagined the door opening at any moment and his aunt and cousins entering the room to find her, but when he did finally open the door, after waiting for her to dress, there was no one there! He called out to see if anyone was near and looked around but found no one.

After this fright, the mood was broken. They sat warming themselves by the fire until the rain stopped, which it did a short while after, then he called the carriage and took her home. They did not speak of what had happened.

The summer passed pleasantly. Isabelle and the prince spent all of their time together; attending parties, boating, riding, swimming in the moonlight and going for long walks. Isabelle also spent occasional afternoons with the old woman in the tower. She had told her all about him and enjoyed the older woman's delight at her stories. She was the only one that the girl confided in, that she and the prince were engaged and to be married once he finished his studies. The old woman had cried then. Isabelle promised her that when she and the prince married they would take her to live with them.

As the summer was drawing to a close, the princess began to worry. She did not look forward to the pain of parting from Charmant. He assured her that he would visit often and would see her during every holiday from school. All too soon their last night together arrived. The king and the queen were away on official business. Isabelle and Charmant were to dine alone in the castle. They took their meal in the east parlor, seated before the fire place. It was a warm moonlit night and the doors were thrown open to the terrace. The room was lit only by candlelight and the light from the fire, but the silver light of the full moon made it seem like daylight outside.

After dinner Charmant and Isabelle went outside and lay side by side on a chaise. They lay there for a long while, gazing out over the lawn, listening to the late summer song of the crickets and the sound of water falling from the enormous fountain that was before them at the bottom of the steps. There was very little breeze; so they decided to cool themselves by taking a dip in the fountain. It was a childish thing to do, and they had fun wading and splashing in the moonlight. They emerged cool and happy, dressed and took up their seats again on the terrace. Isabelle told him of the night she wished on a star for him. He said that he too had wished for her and that being with her was like a long held dream come true. They lay here for a very long time, neither one of them wanting the night to end. There were many tears and long embraces as the dawn broke violently in the east. She walked him out to his carriage, which stood waiting in the drive. They parted with kisses and promises to be together again soon. She stood in the open doorway and watched until his carriage went down the long drive and out of sight.

She called to Xerxes, who had been sleeping by the fire, and went up to bed. She woke late in the afternoon to find that her parents had returned. She joined them for lunch, feeling quite content and happy. It was during lunch that a servant came to the door bearing a large bouquet of wildflowers, the same variety that they he had picked from the field that first day. Her mother made a snide remark about the unusual choice of blooms, but the princess smiled to herself. Charmant knew her and what she liked and loved her for who she was.

King Helios excused himself from the table saying that he was tired. Isabelle noted that he had not been looking very well lately. Moving more slowly, his usually lively step diminished somehow. He asked Isabelle to accompany him to his study. He wanted to speak to her about something. Looking at him and having taken note of his less than perfect health, she was concerned about what he might wish to say to her.

Once in his study, he bade her to sit down. He inquired about how her summer had been and how her studies were coming along. She happily reported all of this to him to include some of the time that she had spent with Charmant. Of course she did not tell him about their secret engagement. The king spoke, a note of concern in his deep voice.

"Isabelle, what are the prince's intentions with you?"

She was caught off guard, "His intentions, what do you mean? He is in love with me." And more quietly, "I assume from things that he has said that he wishes to marry me."

"Did he ask you to marry him?"

"No, not yet, why?"

"Isabelle, you are young and, frankly,

sometimes, too trusting. You have been sheltered from the world, but people are not always what they seem. I am only saying to be careful. Don't rush into anything. Do you understand me?"

Isabelle, a bit taken aback, promised that she would be careful; then she changed the subject. "Father, are you alright? You seem tired lately. I'm worried about you."

The king paused and regarded her for a moment before he spoke. He looked lovingly into her eyes; as always he saw his own eyes staring back. He told her that he was fine. He had been working very hard lately. They had recently established an island colony in the so called "new world;" and her father's fleet ran a supply line to and from this colony, which he had named Orphalese. There had been some trouble with his fleet of merchant ships. Pirates had attacked and looted several of his vessels and made off with a small fortune. He told her that worry over this had taken its toll on him.

She asked if she could help in any way. "I

can always travel for you if you need me to father. You know I'd like nothing more than to go on a mission for you."

The king smiled at her. He had always admired his daughter's lust for adventure. "Thank you, daughter, but there isn't anything you can do right now; but if there is I will let you accompany me on my next trip."

Isabelle was delighted. "Okay father, well, you had better rest up before we have to set sail. I want you to take better care of yourself. You work too hard and worry too much."

She hugged him then and told him how much she loved him. "I love you too Isabelle, very much."

She left him to get some rest and, finding Xerxes outside the door, decided to take him for a walk around the garden where he happily chased the geese and ducks into the pond.

# CHAPTER IV

The next week passed without incident. Isabelle stuck close to home waiting to hear from Charmant. Every day she checked to see if a letter had arrived from him. Every day there was no letter. She tried to ignore her mother's knowing "I told you so" gaze that mocked her as she attempted to feign disinterest in the post.

After two weeks with no letter, Isabelle could take it no longer; so one night she sat down at her desk and wrote Charmant a long letter. She inquired about his studies and his friends and told him everything she had been up to since he left. She told him about her father's troubles with the fleet, of her adventures with Xerxes and Philippides. She told him how she missed him and longed to see him, being careful not to say too much about this lest she appear overly eager. She concluded her letter with love and asked him to write back "If you have time."

Two weeks later a letter finally came from him. It came during lunch. She sat in the dining room with her parents for as long as she could after lunch before taking up the letter off the sideboard and running to her room to read it. Once in her room she locked the door, jumped on the bed, and tore open the letter.

The letter, one page written on heavy stationary in impeccable handwriting read…

*Dear Isabelle,*

*Thank you very much for your letter. I am doing well. School has taken up a great deal of my concentration this term. I am struggling with some advanced classes and barely have time to visit with my friends. I look forward to the end of school when I can leave this place behind and begin my real life. I am not sure if I will be able to visit my aunt in the fall. I had lunch with Lilly the other day. She told me to give you her regards.*

*Charmant*

She sat staring at the letter. What was this? Perhaps he was concerned that her mother might be reading her letters and had not wanted to be too revealing? But surely he could have said more than this! She tried to tell herself that there was a good explanation for this sort of letter; so why did she have a nagging feeling in her stomach? No, she would not jump to conclusions. She must have faith. His feelings for her could not have changed that quickly. What about their wonderful summer? They had spent nearly every day together. He had professed his love for her. He wanted to marry her! Didn't he?

Two more weeks passed with no word from him or of him. She tried her best not to worry, but she did not sleep well during this time and often seemed distracted. She walked around in a daze, a worried expression on her face. Her father was concerned. Her mother knew no other letters came and noted her daughter's strange behavior, but she said nothing. In fact, she acted as if nothing whatsoever was wrong.

One day Isabelle came upon her parents arguing in the study and she listened at the door. It was her father's voice that she made out first. "What do you mean it doesn't matter? I told you I never trusted that boy. He was too much like his father, petty and dishonest."

Her mother interjected "Oh you never liked his father because he had courted me. You were always jealous."

"I was not jealous. I did not like the man and apparently the apple did not fall far from the tree. Oh I know you say Charmant has grown up and changed but I say he is still the same insecure petty tyrant that I came upon when he was a boy. He pretended to be shy but when no one was looking he picked on children smaller than him. I will never forget how he was bullying that poor little boy from the village and when he saw me he tried to act innocent. There was something very devious about him that I can't forget."

"Oh Vata you are making too much of this. He is a normal young man and you are being overprotective."

Her father retorted. "And you are not being protective enough!"

After this the room was silent. Isabelle moved away from the door. Surely her father was wrong. She had never seen this side of Charmant and besides if it had been there he had changed. She had spent enough time with him to know his character, and he was sincere. There had to be a reasonable explanation for his silence. She told herself that in time this would be revealed. She kept trying to believe this, but in time it became harder and harder.

As the leaves began to turn, an invitation arrived for a luncheon at Lady Anne Seaworthy's house. Although Isabelle was in no mood to attend a luncheon party she agreed to go, hoping to get some news of Charmant. Surely he had asked after her to his aunt; and Lady Anne, always fond of Isabelle, would let her know this.

When the occasion for lunch came, Isabelle sat among the other ladies, saying very little. She had not been eating well, and a few of the ladies remarked on her weight loss. She only managed a wan smile and a remark about a diet.

They had been there for over an hour; and Isabelle, unable to stand it any longer, was about to inquire about Charmant when one of the ladies spoke up, "So Lady Anne, I hear there is to be a wedding in your family."

Lady Anne glanced at Isabelle before answering, "Well Helene I don't believe a date has been set yet."

Lady Helene, not about to be daunted said, "Well from what I hear this has been a very long engagement. They had to have set a date by now. If I know the young lady's mother, it will be sooner rather than later. I hear she is rather annoyed that it took so long for Charmant to make the engagement public."

It was as if the air had been sucked out of the room. More than a couple of the ladies stole furtive glances at Isabelle, whose face had gone quite red. She could do nothing but stare straight ahead as the conversation swirled around her. On more than one occasion Lady Anne attempted to steer the conversation in a different direction but the talk raged on.

The story was revealed by Lady Barbara. A wicked gossip, she seemed to know every detail. Apparently, Prince Charmant had been engaged to the daughter of a foreign king for the past year. He and the young woman had met when he was traveling three summers ago and began a long distance courtship. He visited her country on most of his holidays but this summer she had been traveling with her family. From all accounts this princess was stunning. She was heir to her father's throne, having no siblings, but she had no intention of truly ruling her country. Apparently she wanted a husband for this, and the prince fit her profile perfectly. She much preferred the idea of being queen than actually doing the work of a ruler. She had spent her entire childhood being prepared for this role. She eschewed scholarly studies preferring to perfect the art of being a figure-head.

Isabelle sat in stony silence and was only vaguely aware that a question was being directed toward her. It was Lady Silvia. "...well Isabelle should know. Isabelle, you seem to have been quite friendly with Charmant. Do you know anything about when and where the wedding is to be?"

Her face burned as all heads turned toward her. She blinked slowly for a moment, then cleared her throat. Affecting a light and disinterested tone she managed a quiet, "No, you know, I don't know. He mentioned her to me, of course, but I...I don't know."

The queen broke in before it could go on any longer. "Isabelle and Charmant were friends; but, as a gentleman, Charmant would have hardly discussed the details of his engagement with her."

"Well I just thought," said Lady Silvia "that she might know something, having spent so much time with him."

Isabelle was relieved when Lady Anne finally managed to change the subject. She could barely endure the rest of the lunch, but she did. On the way home in the carriage Isabelle sat staring blankly out of the window, tears brimming in her eyes, which had now turned the color of the sea before a storm. Her mother had been going on for some time about the food at the luncheon and what the other ladies had worn, said and done, when Isabelle could take it no more.

Tears began to stream down her face and she turned to her mother "How can you just sit there going on about the stupid lunch? Do you have nothing to say about Charmant's despicable behavior?"

Cythona was taken aback "What are you talking about? What behavior? You mean being friends with you while being engaged to someone else? That is not a crime. Did he make you some promises? Did he lie to you in some way?"

"Yes! He told me he loved me! He said he wanted to be with me…said he would wait for me! I was in love with him, and my heart is breaking, and you sit there prattling on about the luncheon as if nothing happened!?"

"Oh don't be silly." Her mother scolded. "If he really lied to you as you said then he is hardly worth your tears. Is he? Isabelle I have told you over and over. Men will say what they feel they have to, to get what they want. He was here for the summer and wanted someone to have fun with."

Isabelle did not like the way her mother said 'fun.' "Am I being silly mother? He said he wanted to marry me."

"Well he could not have meant it. You should not have taken him seriously. No one can fall in love over one summer. He probably had feelings for you, was fond of you, but he could not have been in love; well obviously he wasn't, was he, or he wouldn't be marrying someone else, now would he?"

This last comment struck Isabelle's heart like a knife. "No I guess you're right. How could he have loved me?"

Oh Isabelle. Stop being so dramatic. You are young. There will be plenty more like him. These things happen, but they are nothing to get worked up about. You are a lady and above all you are a princess. Don't let this affect you, and, certainly if you see him again, don't ever let on that you have given your time with him a second thought. Act as if it meant nothing to you as it clearly meant nothing to him."

Isabelle truly felt as if something inside her was dying. She rode the rest of the way in silence, and when she got home she ran to her room. Without bothering to undress she threw herself on the bed and cried bitterly. She cried for a long time only quieting when she heard her door opening. Xerxes having heard the noise had come up to check on her. He jumped on the bed and began to lick her tear-streaked face. She pushed him away angrily and then felt sorry. She sat up and hugged him to her continuing to cry softly. Eventually she got up, changed her clothes, washed her face and went to visit the old crone in the tower.

Once there, she poured everything out to her. She cried all over again, and the old woman hugged her to her breast. She listened, only commenting every now and then; but mainly she just listened and rocked the child. Isabelle told her of her mother's reaction.

"How could she say that? She knows I loved him. I feel like my heart is breaking."

The old woman held her away from her and wiped her face. "Isabelle. Your mother is doing the best she can." Then more quietly, "Maybe in some ways it's my fault."

"Your fault what do you mean? How can it be your fault?"

The old woman looked at her long and hard as if she was trying to decide something. Then it seemed that she had made a decision. "I mean if I had taught her better…I'm not sure what more I could have done, maybe protected her from her mother, oh I don't know what I meant…never mind."

The girl was confused but she was also very tired now. She was emotionally spent. The old woman offered her some tea and sweets (which the girl declined) then put her to lie down. Isabelle fell into a very deep sleep, and when she awoke it was nighttime, and the old woman had gone to bed. She rose quietly and tiptoed through the cold castle halls toward the family's private chambers. On an impulse she entered her father's study. It was dark except for a small lamp on the desk. She approached the wall and pulled back the heavy amethyst curtain to reveal the small tabernacle there. As she had done so many times in the past she removed the jeweled box and gazed at its sparkling exterior. She traced the butterfly with her finger. Tears welled up in her eyes and splashed on the cold surface as traces of memory came to her. She cried for her childhood and for her former innocence and freedom.

She remembered with some bitterness the time before she had discovered the cuirass. How she would give anything to return to that time. She attempted to do then what she had not done in a very long time. She opened the box slightly; but when she did, was blown away by the power that emanated from it. It was as if, with her neglect, the power had only grown stronger while she had grown weaker. She stumbled backward, and the box fell from her hands with a crash onto the stone floor. It fell on its lid, closing the box tightly. She scrambled to her feet, rushing to lift the box from the floor. After inspecting it to be sure it had suffered no damage, she quickly replaced it in the alcove and drew the curtains before quietly exiting the room. She was confused and somewhat troubled by what had happened. She went to her room, undressed and fell into a very restless sleep. At some point in the night she heard her father come in to check on her. She pretended to sleep as he just sat quietly on the edge of the bed.

# CHAPTER V

Late autumn was now upon them, and she passed the next few weeks her mood alternating between, sorrow, rage and acceptance of what had happened. She contemplated writing angry letters to Charmant demanding an explanation. She imagined going to him and confronting him in person. Those fantasies always ended in some sort of delicious revenge. Eventually these fantasies became fewer. Her tears began to dry up; and, as the rivers and streams began to freeze, her tears ceased to flow entirely. Where there had been pain and grief there was now just a dull, empty spot. Life and her studies resumed, and things were pretty much as they had been before Charmant. By now not one single leaf remained on the trees. Winter, which could no longer be denied, was upon them. The animals of the forest went into hibernation; and a quiet coldness, like death, settled over the entire countryside.

She spent most of her days reading and writing in the library by the fireplace and the afternoons out riding or walking with Xerxes. It was on one of these afternoons after returning from a ride when she entered the house to find everyone in a panic. She was told that her father had collapsed during a meeting with Captain Dejois, one of the commanders of the Royal Navy. He had been taken to his chambers; and the palace doctor, Lord Seaworthy, summoned. She rushed to his rooms to find many people in attendance. Her father lay upon the bed, his eyes closed. He was unconscious and her mother stood nearby, with a tense expression on her face. She was speaking in hushed tones to the doctor. From what Isabelle could gather the doctor was saying that it had something to do with his heart; but Isabelle suspected that this illness emanated from a place that was much deeper and infinitely darker.

She went and sat on the edge of the bed and looked into her father's face. She was shocked to see how aged he looked. Although a man of about seventy, he had always looked young for his age, bright and smiling. She took his hand in hers. He opened his eyes, then and smiled weakly at her. They looked into each other's eyes, neither one speaking. There was no need.

The king recovered slightly from this attack in three days but was to spend the next few weeks confined to his bed. She and the queen took turns sitting with him. When the queen was not by his side, she was in a frenzy, having hushed tense exchanges with her royal advisors. From what Isabelle overheard she imagined her mother was readying affairs of state in the eventuality of the king's death. Although she was worried for her father she had no doubt that he would recover. He was a strong man with an even stronger spirit. Even when his illness dragged on and he seemed to deteriorate more each day, she felt hopeful that he would recover by the spring.

There were other troubles brewing as well. The increasingly frequent attacks on their ships by pirates and her father's illness were weakening her country. Her father's most trusted captain, Admiral Gravely, who was responsible for overseeing the safe passage of their merchant fleet, was then killed while bringing precious cargo back to Xamayca from Orphalese. It was rumored that the dreaded pirate Captain Flint, who flew under the flag of the sleeping dragon, was responsible and that in fact he had invaded Orphalese; but no one could be sure, because not a man had been left to tell the true account and no one had been able to bring Flint to justice. Without the king, no one dared to make the voyage between Xamayca and the colony, and the inhabitants, cut off from much needed supplies, were dying. If things did not change soon there would be no colony to speak of, and the strength of the empire might not recover.

Isabelle felt certain that she could command their fleet if given a chance, but she did not dare mention such a thing. Besides, she was certain that her father would recover and all would be right in the kingdom.

One day she was sitting in the window seat in her father's chamber day dreaming of just this. She imagined doing battle with the dreaded Captain Flint and successfully conveying her father's ships to Orphalese and saving the island's inhabitants. Her reverie was interrupted by her father's voice. When she turned around she realized that he must have been awake for some time and had lain in bed staring at her there in the window seat.

"Isa?" his voice sounded stronger than it had in some time "How are you?"

Although his concern was always genuine, something about the way he asked this question troubled her. Attempting to appear cheerful, she told him that she was fine and asked how he was feeling.

He looked out of the window for a moment before saying, "I'm ready to go there."

"It's awfully cold outside father. It will be better to go out in the spring. We can go for one of our walks then."

He shook his head slowly "I don't mean outside. You know what I mean. I'm ready to leave this, to unwrap." He was gesturing at his body.

She went over and sat on the bed and took his hand. "I'm not ready for you to go yet. I…we need you here. Who will command your fleet? Who will take care of me?"

"Isabelle. I love you more than anything and I don't want to leave you or your mother, but you will be alright. I want you to know that you have been the best daughter any man could have ever wished for. You are my darling Isabelle; but the time has come."

He moved aside the cover then, and she saw the blue morpho. "The time has come to give you what is rightfully yours."

She began to protest to tell him that he would get better but he stopped her. "No. You must have faith that everything will be alright. Isn't that what you always tell me, to have faith? You have everything you need to carry on."

She wanted so much to be brave but she fell upon him and began to sob. He hugged her tight. "I will always love you and I will always be with you. Nothing can stop that. Do you remember what I told you when you were a little girl and we walked on the beach?"

She sniffed back her tears "You told me that you would walk through hell and back for me."

"Yes. I don't want you to ever forget that. I want you to take this box. It's time for it to be in your possession. What you do with it is up to you, but it is time for it to leave my chamber. Your mother said that you were not ready, you know your mother, but I know that you are."

She told him then how much she loved him and how grateful she was that he was her father. She told him that on some level she knew that she had wished for him as her father before she was even born.

"I wished for you too Isa."

They sat quietly like this for some time until he fell asleep. She was sitting, holding his hand when her mother came in and put her hand on her shoulder. She looked into her mother's face, now a mask of sorrow. The princess stood up, gave her a hug then left the queen with her husband and went to bed.

Isabelle was roused from her sleep just before the crack of dawn. A servant was sent to get her. The Sun King had died. She dressed quickly and ran to his chamber. She met her mother at the door who tried to hold her back from the kings' bed but she pushed passed her and ran sobbing to her father's side. She stared into her father's face, but she could see that he was gone. She touched his hand and was shocked to discover that it had grown cold already. His great light had gone out, and all that remained was a shell. Her mind could not conceive of this. She ran then to her mother who held her as she cried. She could not recall a time before when this had happened, and even through her grief she noted how good it felt.

The spell was broken all too soon.

The queen told her, "You are going to have to be strong now. We have much to do to prepare for the state funeral." The queen launched into a litany of what would have to be done.

Isabelle, unable to take it, pushed away from her mother angrily. Her father was dead and her heart was breaking. She did not give a damn about state funerals.

She then ran from the room and down the hall. She did not stop running until she got to the stables. She flung open the door to Philippides' stall, tore off his blanket, grabbed a handful of his black mane and swung her leg over his back. She had no idea where she was going or what she was doing as she set out in the cold blue light of dawn. All she knew was that she had to get away. She gave Philippides a hard kick and gripping tightly to his mane, they tore out of the stable yard. His hoofs echoed on the frozen ground. She crossed the wide front yard, headed out of the palace gates, and eventually found herself in the forest. She was oblivious to the cold and to the branches that tore her clothes and whipped her face. She pushed her horse on, leaving the woods behind. They ran for miles and did not stop until they reached the edge of Crystal Falls.

There she dismounted and was overtaken by the grief that she had attempted to outrun. She turned her face toward the heavens as if looking for an answer there. Tears streamed down her face, and she cried as she had never cried before. She cried until she could cry no more. She found herself huddled at the base of a tree; an odd feeling of peace had suddenly washed over her. The forest was so still. The only sound was the water hitting the rocks far beneath her at the foot of the falls. Her eye suddenly caught a movement in the trees. On closer inspection she saw that it was a Red-tailed hawk. She found this strange as she had only seen them before on the edges of the fields. The bird turned its head and looked at her with an almost knowing expression. The young woman and the bird regarded each other for a moment until Isabelle became aware of the cold. Her tears had begun to freeze on her cheeks.

She called for Philippides, mounted him, and turned toward the castle. She walked him, at first slowly then began to trot. She was aware that the hawk was following them, flying from tree to tree and emitting an occasional screech. She felt that the creature was playing with her, and she began to ride faster and faster to see if it would follow. As she crossed the final field before reaching the gate, Philippides was charging at breakneck speed. Isabelle realized that one misstep now could be deadly, but oddly she did not care. She was aware of a growing feeling of joy welling up inside of her. She urged her horse on faster and faster. She was recalling her childhood days, running races with her father on the sidelines, urging her on to the finish line. She could see his loving eyes, his encouraging smile. She knew the hawk was keeping pace with her although she could barely see it out of the corner of her eye.

The sun was rising over the hills now and it had begun to snow. Suddenly a fierce wind kicked up and a small tornado of swirling snow-flakes was by her side. She was over-taken by joy and began to laugh as she be-came aware of her father's presence beside her, racing with her, urging her on. He was playing with her. She was laughing and crying at the same time. The tornado now engulfed her, swirled around her, tickling her, holding her and loving her. She could just make out the palace gate ahead. Her father was chal-lenging her to a race, telling her to go faster and to finish strong, as he did when she was a child and he was teaching her foot racing. They were neck and neck. But then as now he was only pretending that she could beat him, that she could run faster than him; but she drove on and with a final kick just made it through the gate before him.

She was laughing hard now and turned to him to say something, when, just as sudden-ly as it had come, the wind died down. The swirling tornado of snow was no longer be-side her. She looked back to see it hovering at the gate for a brief moment; then it was gone. She felt the joy recede from her. He would not follow her this time. He had gone as far as he could. She would have to go on alone now.

The next five days were a blur as the household prepared for the funeral. Dignitaries and statesmen came in from all over, and many important meetings were held between her mother and her new advisors who had once belonged to the king. Isabelle spent as much time as she could away from it all, preferring the warmth of the old woman's room.

She sat stoically through the funeral at her mother's side, wearing a stiff black dress of paramatta trimmed with crepe. She endured long speeches by those who did not even know her father. Her mother did not weep, tears being reserved for private times. The princess was touched, however, by those who came up to her later to offer their condolences and to say kind words about her father. After the last of the guests had gone her mother and her advisors retired to her father's study. Isabelle followed.

Apparently the trouble in Orphalese had

reached a critical point. They had postponed action for as long as they could. If something was not done soon, the colony would be taken over by the buccaneers led by Captain Flint; and the inhabitants, turned into slaves. Other islands in the region had succumbed to this, and the tales were horrifying. With her father's death and the death of Admiral Gravely, there was no one whom the queen trusted to organize their navy and to convey their fleet of merchant vessels to the island.

One of her advisors was in favor of forming an allegiance with a neighboring kingdom that could supply the navy; but to enter into this bargain would mean a loss of control of her kingdom, and the queen was against this. Another advisor suggested that they cut their losses in Orphalese, rather than shed any more blood; but this might signal the end of their burgeoning empire to their enemies and allies alike, and the queen also abhorred this solution.

Half turning toward Isabelle the queen muttered, "If only there was a prince to take your father's place. If I had been blessed to have a son none of this would be happening."

Isabelle knew just what had to be done. "I'll go mother. I will organize the navy and I will re-open the supply lines to Orphalese."

Her mother looked at her daughter as if she had lost her mind. She told her that under no circumstances was she to even consider such a thing and to never mention this preposterous idea again.

Isabelle smoldered with rage. "Who then? This is what I was trained for. I was prepared by my father's side. I know what has to be done, and what I don't know I will learn."

After some consideration, the queen's advisors suggested that this was a viable solution, but the queen would hear none of it. Even with the backing of the advisors and Captain Dejois, the remaining commander of the navy, she refused.

Isabelle and Cythona got into a blazing argument, neither of them willing to back down. Isabelle finally stormed from the room. Returning to her own chambers, her mind made up, she tore off her mourning clothes. She would not command the respect of the navy and the other sailors wearing a gown. Grabbing up a large pair of scissors she lopped off her shoulder length hair. She pulled on her black leather breeches and stuffed a few other pairs in a bag. She donned a man's shirt and waistcoat over her bodice and grabbed her longest and heaviest coat. This she tucked into her closet. With or without her mother's blessing she would leave at dawn, but first she must say good bye to her old friend.

It was late but she knew that she would be up waiting for her. Isabelle told her what happened and what she was about to do. The old woman would miss her terribly but she understood that she had to go. Isabelle did not want to leave her either but knew she must. They said a tearful good bye and hugged for a long time. Isabelle promised to write to her as soon as she was able. She was almost down the stairs when she heard it, "Walk good."

When she returned to her room she was

shocked to see her mother sitting on her bed.

"What are you doing here mother? If you've come to stop me it won't work. I have the support of those I will command and I am going."

Her mother looked at her wearily and bid her to sit down.

"Isabelle, I have not come to stop you. Of course I don't want you to go but I will not forbid it. I have just lost my husband and I don't want to lose you too, that's why I tried to stop you, but I understand that you must go. I came to say good bye. I will not be seeing you off at dawn because I don't think my heart can take it, but I wanted to tell you good bye now and to wish you luck."

Isabelle could not have been more shocked. She stared at her mother for a long time before throwing her arms about her and bursting into tears. "I don't want to leave you either mother, but I must go. All will be well. Father's spirit will be with me."

The queen held her for a moment then

stood to leave. "I do love you, you know?"

"I know mother. I love you too."

After her mother had gone Isabelle called Xerxes to her and the two of them lay in the middle of the bed to take a nap. She meant to sleep for just a moment but she fell into a deep sleep. She awoke to the sound of tapping on her window and instantly realized that the sun was rising and it was time to go. She went to the window and opened it to find the Red-tailed hawk from the woods sitting on the ledge. She put out her arm and the bird jumped onto her fist.

"Well, Xerses. It looks like we have a new member of the family. What shall we name her?"

Xerxes only cocked his head at her (in those days he could not speak but could project his thoughts). "Almitra you say? Alright then Almitra, are you ready for an adventure?"

The bird looked at her with her intelligent eyes. Isabelle took this as a yes; so she finished getting her things together, placed Almitra onto her shoulder, and set off for the stables where she ladened Philippides down with her packs (one containing her magic box). She paused at the palace gates to look back at the place where she had grown up. It would be a long time before she would see it again.

It was a very cold winter morning as she set off for the port of Abukir. She rode out of the palace gates upon Philippides' back with Almitra on her shoulder and Xerxes at her heels.

# ABOUT THE AUTHOR

 Dr. Nicole Cutts licensed Clinical Psychologist, Success Coach, Speaker, Artist and Organizational Consultant inspires and empowers people to achieve a more balanced and successful lifestyle. Nicole enjoys taking clients to the "Aha" moment, helping them identify blocks, spark a change in attitude and behavior and ramp up personal performance. She has consulted with and trained executives, managers, and teams at Fortune 500 Companies, Federal Government Agencies, and Non-Profit Organizations. As a Master Facilitator, Speaker and Success Coach, she helps people create an exceptional life by honoring their mind, body, and spirit so they can experience joy, passion, meaning, and ultimate success in their work. She was named 2011 Entrepreneur of the Year by The National Black MBA Association's DC Chapter and one of Tagg Magazine's Most Enterprising Women in 2015.

Nicole has made several media appearances on radio and television to include BET's The Center, the BBC, Roland S. Martin's Urban Business Roundtable, The Steve Harvey Morning Show and The Daily Drum. Nicole is the co-host of the Inside Out radio show on Washington, DC's WPFW 89.3 fm (www.wpfw.org).

She is also a frequently quoted expert on success in national publications. She has co-authored and published several articles and stories in scientific and literary journals. She has been a featured writer on Corporate Wellness, Success Coaching, and Diversity on several business websites and was the Senior Features Editor at The Diversity Channel. She is a former faculty member of The University of MD, Baltimore County where she taught in the Women's Studies Dept.

An avid yoga practitioner, she ignites change, using somatic coaching principles helping people create an exceptional life. It is her dedication to well-being and belief that we should find joy and passion in our work that motivated her to start Cutts Consulting, LLC in 2002. She created Vision Quest Retreats in 2009 to help women discover their passion and purpose and bring this to life through their work.

Dr. Cutts, received her Ph.D. from the California School of Professional Psychology-LA, where her emphasis of study was Multicultural Community Clinical Psychology. She received her Executive Coach certification from The Center for Executive Coaching. She also holds a B.S. in Psychology from Howard University.

Made in the USA
Middletown, DE
11 December 2018